LFA Health

T'ai Chi]

Movements 1 -

Explained in an easy to follow format

By Sheila Dickinson
President of the LFA Health Arts

Benefits:-
Helps to improve balance and co-ordination
Increases stamina and flexibility
Improves the cardiovascular system
Eases Stress
Provides Relaxation

Printed and published in Great Britain by

PO BOX 19,
HEDON,
HULL
HU12 8YR

First Published 2003

Published by Stairway Distribution Limited
PO Box 19, Hedon. Hull. HU12 8YR
www.leefamilyarts.com

ISBN 1-903711-07-X

Please consult your Doctor before taking part in the following exercise programme.
The LFA and Stairway Distribution Ltd disclaim any liability for loss or injury in connection with the advice and exercises included in this book.

Acknowledgements

To the past Masters of our Arts - we offer our sincere thanks!

Books by the same author:-

T'AI CHI FORM	(MOVEMENTS 1 TO 140)
T'AI CHI DANCE	(MOVEMENTS 1 TO 184)
T'AI CHI STICK	(MOVEMENTS 1 TO 150)
T'AI CHI SILK	(MOVEMENTS 1 TO 156)
T'AI CHI SWORD	(MOVEMENTS 1 TO 108)
T'AI CHI NUNCHAKU	(MOVEMENTS 1 TO 150)
T'AI CHI FAN	(MOVEMENTS 1 TO 150)

CHANG MING T'AI CHI LONG LIFE DIET AND RECIPE BOOK

VIDEOS by the same author:-

T'AI CHI FORM	(MOVEMENTS 1 TO 50)
T'AI CHI DANCE	(MOVEMENTS 1 TO 50)
T'AI CHI STICK	(MOVEMENTS 1 TO 50)
T'AI CHI SILK	(MOVEMENTS 1 TO 50)
T'AI CHI SWORD	(MOVEMENTS 1 TO 50)

Available from: -

Stairway Distribution Limited
P O Box 19
Hedon
Hull
HU12 8YR
Tel / Fax 01482 896063

Or visit our Website www.leefamilyarts.com with full secure ordering facilities; which also shows details of the:-

LFA Weekend Courses
LFA Summer Courses
LFA Easter Course
LFA Trainee Instructor Courses

THE LFA T'AI CHI LIBRARY

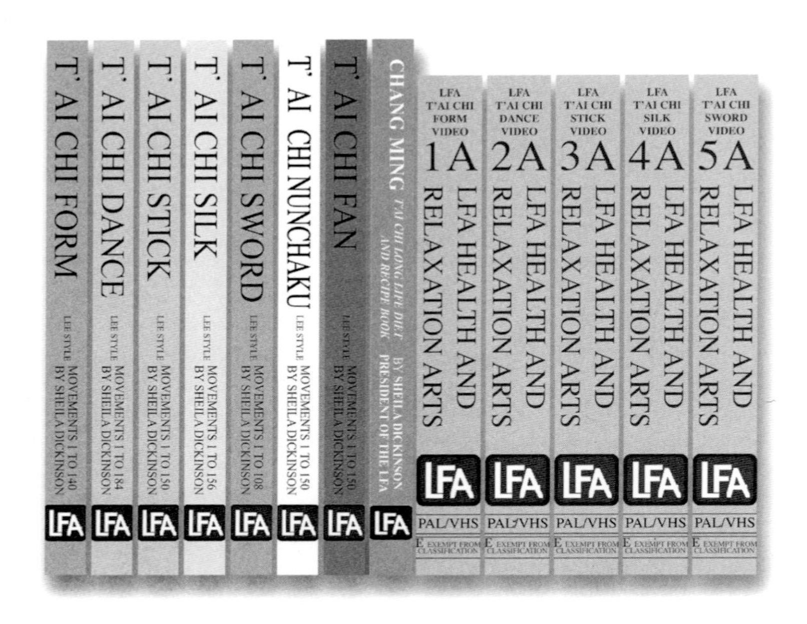

CONTENTS

Foreword

Welcome to the Lee Family Arts T'ai Chi Fan Set. Please note, I have used the same foreword in each of my books in order that I can pay tribute to my late Grand Master, Chee Soo.

My position as President of the Lee Family Arts started in January 1995. Since that time, I have had the privilege to guide my fellow instructors in all aspects of LFA T'ai Chi, and I have worked hard to reach as many people as possible, so that everyone may gain from the many health benefits of our Arts.

I would not be writing this book today without the guidance and patience of my late Grand Master Chee Soo, who spent most of his life teaching the Lee Family Arts. Chee Soo is in my thoughts constantly and I offer my sincere thanks for receiving the benefit of his wisdom and understanding.

Chee Soo wrote five books published by the Aquarian Press, sadly at the time of writing only one title remains in print today 'The Chinese Art of T'ai Chi Ch'uan'. In this book he traces the history of the Lee Style back to Ho-Hsieh Lee circa 1,000 BC. It is stated that the Lee Family have always been Taoists and that the Lee Style is a Yin and Yang style, this means that everything within it is in complete balance and harmony.

Chee Soo occasionally spoke of his own Grand Master, Chan Kam Lee and told of how they had met during 1934 in Hyde Park in London. In those days there were very few Oriental people in London and the two became friends. It was a friendship that would change Chee Soo's life forever. After Chan Kam Lee's death, Chee Soo dedicated himself to maintaining the knowledge and wisdom which he had learnt from Chan Kam Lee.

While staying with my family and my self, Chee Soo talked to me about the future of the Lee Family Arts and the direction he wished them to take. On Monday the 16th May 1994 Chee Soo asked me to give him my word that I would not let the Lee Family Arts die.

Sadly Chee Soo died on the 29th August 1994.

It is with the greatest respect to Chee Soo that I offer my own writings and understanding of the lessons he taught me.

The names of Instructors who have trained, qualified and still maintain their own training can be obtained from the Lee Family Arts official register of qualified instructors. The LFA can only vouch for the quality and content of that which is taught within an official LFA registered class.

The Lee Family Arts have been tried and tested for

thousands of years before we were born. The people who teach them are merely caretakers, who have the privilege of maintaining the Arts, and witnessing them helping others.
This book teaches you the first one hundred and fifty movements of the LFA T'ai Chi Fan Set. There are three hundred movements in total and these latter movements will be explained in further publications. The Lee Family Arts will always be known as a Family Art and it is a family which grows in numbers daily. In concluding, I would like to say a very special welcome to you!

The Importance of You

Who is the most important person in the universe? As far as you are concerned it is you. Even before you were born, you competed in a great race at the time of your conception, nature declared you a WINNER.

Perhaps we ought to remember this fact and realise that we live in a world full of winners.

In a world of plenty, millions starve, do the starving feel like winners?

It is not only the starving or poverty stricken who carry the weight of the world on their shoulders. Look around in our country where we eat for pleasure, have more leisure time than ever before, are we a nation of happy people? Do we act like a nation of winners?

If every individual undertook the ultimate responsibility and made sure that they looked after their own health, there would not be such a drain on the health service.

You are an incredible person with such great potential; you also have the ability to help yourself. We are not suggesting that people receiving medical treatment should discontinue it, what we are suggesting is that you help yourself to help your doctor to help you.

You have a mind and a body, use them and look for a healthier life style. The Chang Ming diet is an excellent health diet which has been around for thousands

of years and I have seen it help many people. The time when you need your T'ai Chi and the Chang Ming Diet most is when you are ill - USE IT!
In the West we are taught to rest and go to bed if we do not feel well. My late Master always made me work through illness.
I have not personally taken any medication since nineteen eighty. If I feel out of sorts I use the Chinese remedies as shown in the 'First Aid' section of the Chang Ming T'ai Chi Long Life Diet and Recipe Book. The nice thing is that we work with western medicine and several doctors have suggested to their patients that they should attend my classes.
We have specialised breathing exercises to help you to harmonise your breathing with your movements. With each movement and each breath, listen to what is going on inside you; it takes time to understand what is happening within yourself.
People start to gain from the moment they practice their very first movement in the Lee Family Arts; initially you are learning the mechanics of the movements and a basic understanding of what your own energy feels like.
Advance students learn how to use and understand the benefits of harmonising their Chi energy with the

external Li energy, which is free energy from the Cosmos. Just like gravity, electricity and magnetism, it has been given to man and women kind to enhance their lives. The Chinese nation has known how to use and enhance these energies and have been very adept at keeping them to themselves for the past 3000 years. Using the exercises of the LFA Health Arts, we can help you to help yourself. The responsibility of teaching the Lee Family Arts lies with me, the responsibility of learning the lessons offered by the Lee Family Arts, lies with you.

The rewards are not ones of material gain, a much greater gift is on offer. It is written, that a Sage fetched water and chopped wood, became enlightened, fetched water and chopped wood. A valuable lesson is written within those words.

When you are fully able to harmonise your Chi and Li energy, you will be able to move your energy to any part of your body at will. Therefore, when you experience pain (physical or emotional - which is the bodies signal that help is required), you will be able to move your Chi energy from your Tan Tien (also called the Lower Cauldron i.e. the area below your naval), to the area of pain and feel the healing commence, culminating in the alleviation of the pain.

Subsequently, you will also be able to use your energy to heal others.
You will also be able to see far more than that which is in front of your eyes, and have a greater understanding of the true inner you.
By the very definition of the word creatures (which we are), we are all here on earth to be creative (not destructive or self-destructive). Therefore we are here to make our world and ourselves better places to be and better places to live.
Imagine a world where all the people take the responsibility for their own heath and eat and drink in a manner which respects their gift of creation.

Taoist Walk

In the LFA we teach the importance of the Taoist Walk, it is included in every book written in this series. The principles of the Taoist Walk apply to all aspects of our health. For example, when the Taoist Walk is harmonised with our specialised breathing exercises and hand movements (which are taught within our classes), it helps to boost the vigour of the immune system. Another exercise, when combined with the Taoist Walk, benefits the heart. We also have specialised movements which, while helping to rejuvenate different parts of the body, also provide quite dynamic self defence techniques.

Taoist Walk

The Taoist walk is an extremely important part of the LFA health training because it moves the weight from one leg to another in a special and subtle way. Not only is one leg working while the other one rests, but the working leg is the Yang leg and the resting leg is the Yin leg.

The weight is moved from one leg to the other before you try to alter the position of your foot.

Start with your feet slightly wider than shoulder width apart, toes pointing forwards. Both hands are held at waist height with the palms facing each other.

1/ Drift your weight across to your right side, your right knee bends, your hips and your bottom move across to the right side.

2/ Now take a very small step forwards with your left foot, placing your heel down first. Allow your left knee to bend, move your hips and bottom across to the left. Keep your right leg straight, do not lock your right knee.

Practise walking across the room in this manner. People suffering from back, hip, knee and ankle problems, reap great benefits from practising the Taoist Walk.

We use the Taoist Walk in all of our form sets. With practise it can be incorporated into your every day walk (so that it is undetectable), only you will know the benefits you are receiving each time you place one foot in front of the other.

The Taoist Walk helps to move your Chi energy into the lower part of your body. In the West we tend to carry a lot of energy congestion around the pelvic area, this stagnation leads to the above mentioned problems. So it is a good idea to learn to walk the Taoist Way.

Please try it for yourself, especially if you wake up in the morning feeling stiff, a few minutes practising the Taoist Walk could help to make you feel like a new man or woman.

Etiquette

The etiquette is something which has been handed down through the centuries along with the T'ai Chi, I personally feel it represents a respect for the Arts we are practising and the ancient Masters to whom we owe so much.

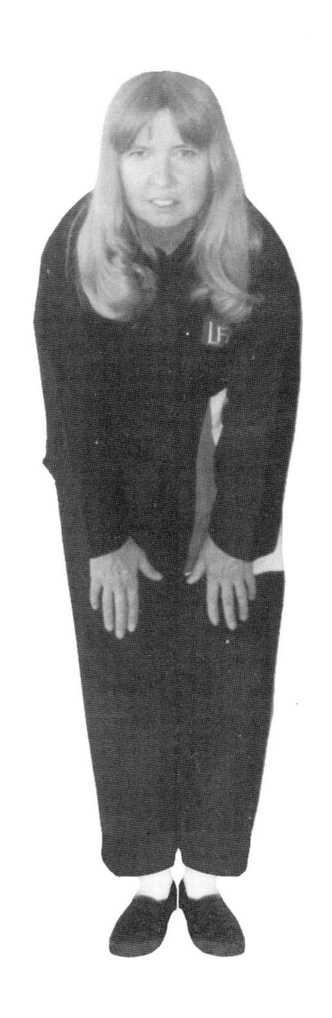

When entering or leaving a training hall a student should bow to the room. This bow consists of bending forwards from the waist, at the same time, both palms rest on your thighs.

If you arrive after a class has already started you should walk round to the front of the hall, bow to the person taking the class and wait for them to bow to you in return (using the bow explained below).

At the beginning of a class the bow consists of placing your right arm on top of your left in front of your body, your right palm faces down, and your left palm faces up.

When training with a partner you should both bow to each other at the start and finish (using the same bow as when entering and leaving the training room).

If an instructor offers you guidance with your training, you should bow to them after they have finished teaching you, (again using the bow for entering and leaving the training room).

LFA T'ai Chi Fan Set

The LFA T'ai Chi Fan set is the set which develops your stamina to a high level. As mentioned several times in this book it is important to listen to your own body and ensure that you do not strain.

The LFA Health Arts are both complex and specialised. Within all of our disciplines we have movements which are based on Chinese medicine and which are designed to improve your health.

When new people come to my classes, I ask them why they have decided to try T'ai Chi, the answers are varied, yet each person has some ailment (whether emotional or physical) from back pains, asthma, insomnia etc. to stress related problems. I encourage them to progress at their own pace and avoid the western world concept of seeing everything as a competition. Students of LFA T'ai Chi find that it does not matter what the person next to you is doing, it is your body which counts; take everything one step at a time. Progress is not based on the quantity of movements that you know or the speed at which you learn them. Without good health, we have nothing, it is easy to put things off for another day. Put yourself first, start your training today, in so doing you will not only help yourself but you will also help everyone who makes up your world, your life and your family. The LFA Website www.leefamilyarts.com has twentyseven pages, most of them with free video clips which teach you exercises to help bring relief from a variety of ailments.

I was recently asked why I had put such valuable information in the public domain, the answer is because the Lee Family Arts are dedicated to helping people. This is why we continue to invest in producing books and videos which can help everyone. For up-to-date information of LFA T'ai Chi classes, products and workshops, please visit our website.

LFA T'ai Chi Stances

Although you may be eager to press on and learn the beneficial movements of our Fan set, it is important that you take the time to familiarise yourself with the stances.

First become familiar with their names, next check the position of your feet. It is important that you have the correct weight distribution without any strain on your body. If you attend a weekly class, your instructor will be able to advise you. However if you are unable to attend classes, I suggest you stand in front of a mirror to help you to achieve a good posture.

It is important to remember that our feet provide our roots, without which we will fall over. Take the time to move from one stance to another applying the Taoist Walk, only in this way will you reap the full benefits which are on offer to everyone.

In these early stages of your training, try to feel what is happening to the muscles of your body as you move slowly from one position to the next. Later on you will appreciate a far greater depth to the movements you are practising. The person who takes their time and learns patience will eventually achieve a far greater benefit from our Arts than the person who rushes on believing they know all the movements of a particular form set. Judging your progress by numbers is very much a western concept, the LFA are purely interested in improving the quality of your life. There is no time limit, or pressure applied to your journey with us. Enjoy learning and practising our Arts, and find the path to a different way of living.

Bear Stance

Bear stance is achieved by standing with your feet shoulder width apart. Your body should be relaxed with no tension. Both of your arms should be hanging loosely by your sides. You should be looking straight ahead.

We use Bear stance at the beginning of all of our sets, when we adopt the 'Prepare' position.

Bee Stance

Bee stance is achieved, by standing with both heels together, and your toes pointing slightly outwards, with both knees bent. Both arms hang loosely by your sides. Your eyes should be looking straight ahead.

Cat Stance

To achieve a Right Cat stance, the left leg is bent at the knee, the heel is raised on your right foot. The ball of the right foot rests lightly on the floor with eighty percent of your weight on your left leg.

To achieve a Left Cat stance, the right leg is bent at the knee, the heel is raised on your left foot. The ball of your left foot rests lightly on the floor with eighty percent of your weight on your right leg.

Crane Stance

To achieve a Right Crane stance move your weight onto your left leg (bending your left knee slightly to aid your balance). At the same time raise your right leg (bending your right knee) until your thigh is parallel with the floor. Students who have difficulty balancing should use a Cat stance for movements which require one leg to be lifted off the floor.

To achieve a Left Crane stance take your weight onto your right leg (bending your right knee slightly to aid your balance). At the same time raise your left leg (bending your left knee) until your thigh is parallel with the floor.

Crossed Legs Stance

To achieve Right Crossed Legs stance, bend your left knee slightly. Now cross your right leg in front of and slightly beyond your left leg, raise the heel of your right foot.

To achieve Left Crossed Legs stance, bend your right knee slightly. Now cross your left leg in front of and slightly beyond your right leg, raise the heel of your left foot.

Dog Stance

To achieve Right Dog stance move your weight onto your left leg (bending your knee slightly to aid your balance). At the same time extend and raise your right leg forwards, your leg should be at a height which is comfortable to you without strain. To achieve Left Dog stance, move your weight onto your right leg (bending your knee slightly to aid your balance). At the same time extend and raise your left leg forwards.

Dragon Stance

To achieve a Right Dragon stance step forwards from either a Bear or an Eagle stance. It is important not to overstep, make sure that you have a good gap (width ways) between your feet.

Drift your weight over to your right side, so that your weight is spread between your right hip, knee and ankle. Eighty percent of your weight should be on your right leg, your left leg should be straight although not locked.

To achieve a Left Dragon stance, follow the same procedure as above this time stepping forward with your left leg.

Duck Stance

To achieve a Right Duck stance from Eagle stance, step behind with your left foot, placing your heel down first. Now drift your weight onto your left leg (bending your knee), your right leg should be straight, although not locked. To achieve a Left Duck stance from Eagle stance, step back with your right foot, placing your heel down first. Now drift your weight onto your right leg (bending your knee), your left leg should be straight, although not locked.

Drunkard Stance

To achieve Drunkard stance simply lay on your back on the floor with both arms by your sides.

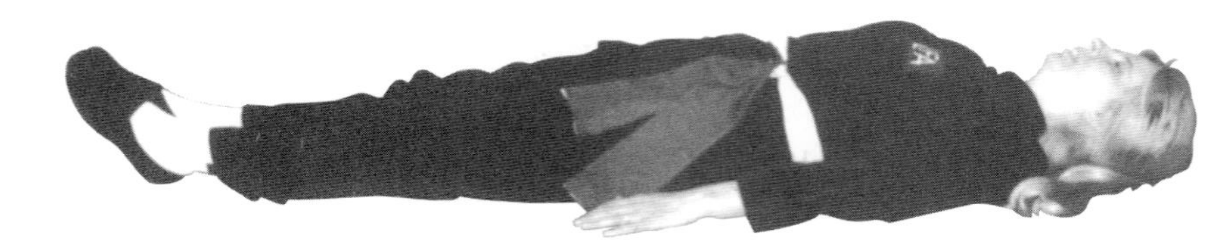

Eagle Stance

Eagle stance, place both heels together, toes pointing slightly outwards. Your weight should be evenly balanced between both legs.

Fish Stance

To achieve a Right Fish stance lie on your right side and support your head with your right hand.
To achieve a Left Fish stance simply lie on your left side and support your head with your left hand (see photograph).

Frog Stance

To achieve a frog stance, stand with your feet slightly wider than shoulder width apart, now bend both knees and lower your weight down. Remember to listen to your own body and do not strain.

Hawk Stance

To achieve a Right Hawk stance, move your weight onto your left leg (bending your knee slightly to aid your balance). Next move your right leg out directly behind you (bending your body forward to create a natural line between your leg and your spine). Please remember that there should be no strain, listen to your own body.

To achieve a Left Hawk stance, move your weight onto your right leg (bending your knee slightly to aid your balance). Next move your left leg out directly behind you.

Horse Stance

To achieve a Right Horse stance move your weight onto your left leg (bending the knee slightly to aid your balance). Now take your right leg out sideways (see photograph).
To achieve a Left Horse stance move your weight onto your right leg (bending the knee slightly to aid your balance). Now take your left leg out sideways.

Leg Triangle Stance

Your feet should be slightly wider than shoulder width apart, with your weight evenly distributed between both legs.

Leopard Stance

To achieve a Right Leopard stance take a pace off sideways to your right (bending your right knee and drifting your weight across). At the same time straighten your left leg.

To achieve a Left Leopard stance take a pace off sideways to your left (bending your left knee and drifting your weight across). At the same time straighten your right leg.

Lotus Stance

Lotus stance is achieved by sitting down with your legs forward and then drawing them into your body with the soles of the feet together.

Monkey Stance

To achieve a Right Monkey stance step back with your left leg (bending your left knee). Your right leg is straight with the toes of your right foot raised.

To achieve a Left Monkey stance step back with your right leg (bending your right knee). Your left leg is straight with the toes of your left foot raised.

Praying Mantis Stance

To achieve Praying Mantis stance, kneel down on both knees and sit on your feet.

Riding Horse Stance

To achieve a Riding Horse stance, stand with both feet slightly wider than shoulder width apart (both knees bent) your weight should be evenly distributed between both legs. Your body should be relaxed, without strain.

Scissors Stance

To achieve a Right Scissors stance drift your weight onto your left leg (bending your knee slightly). Now cross your right leg behind and slightly beyond your left leg, raising the heel of your right foot.

To achieve a Left Scissors stance drift your weight onto your right leg (bending your knee slightly). Now cross your left leg behind and slightly beyond your right leg, raising the heel of your left foot.

Sitting Down Crossed Legs Stance

To achieve sitting down crossed legs stance sit on the floor with both legs crossed (your left leg is furthest away from you).

Snake Stance

To achieve a Right Snake stance take a small pace forwards with your right leg. Both knees are slightly bent, your weight is evenly distributed between both legs.

To achieve a Left Snake stance take a small pace forwards with your left leg. Both knees are slightly bent, your weight is evenly distributed between both legs.

Stork Stance

To achieve a Right Stork stance move your weight onto your left leg (bending your left knee slightly to aid your balance). Now raise and bend your right leg moving your foot behind you.

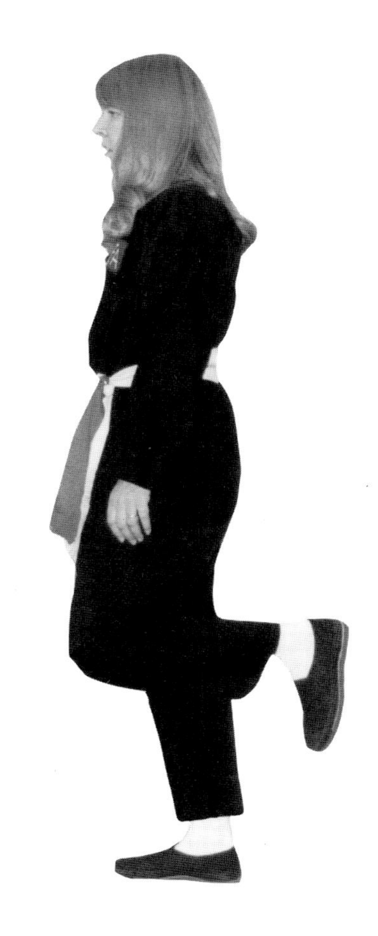

To achieve a Left Stork stance move your weight onto your right leg (bending your right knee slightly to aid your balance). Now raise and bend your left leg moving your foot behind you.

Turtle Stance

To achieve a Turtle stance kneel on the floor and move your body forwards until the palms of your hands rest on the floor, directly beneath your shoulders.

Willow Stance

To achieve a Willow stance lie on the floor and raise your legs up in the air, supporting the base of your spine with both hands. Please do not strain.

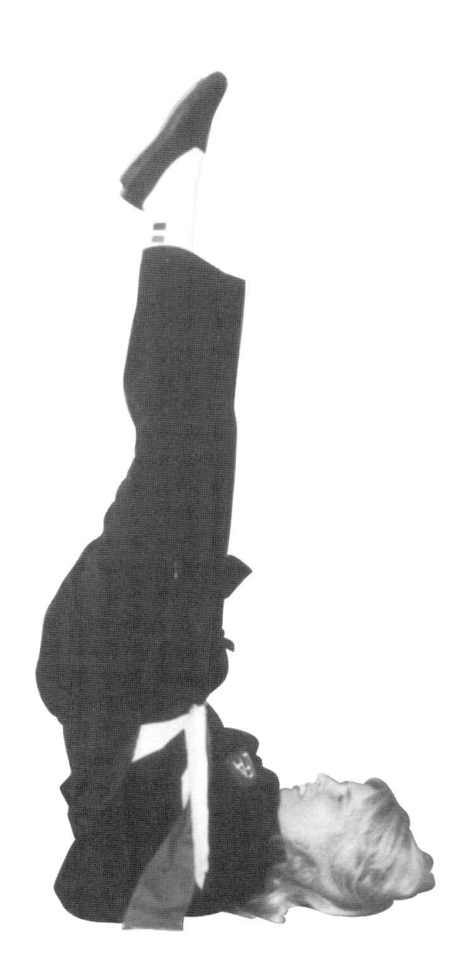

List of Stances 1 – 150

1	Eagle
2	Eagle
3	Right Cat
4	Right Dragon
5	Right Duck
6	Left Duck
7	Right Crossed Legs
8	Left Dragon
9	Right Crane
10	Right Dog
11	Left Duck
12	Right Duck
13	Left Crane
14	Left Crane
15	Left Horse
16	Left Crane
17	Left Hawk
18	Left Crane
19	Left Dog
20	Left Crossed Legs
21	Right Horse
22	Right Crane
23	Right Hawk
24	Right Crane

25	Right Dog
26	Right Crossed Legs
27	Left Chicken
28	Drunkard
29	Left Fish
30	Left Fish
31	Left Fish
32	Turtle
33	Turtle
34	Praying Mantis
35	Left Dragon
36	Right Crossed Legs
37	Bear
38	Right Scissors
39	Bear
40	Right Crossed Legs
41	Bear
42	Right Scissors
43	Bear
44	Right Crossed Legs
45	Bear
46	Eagle
47	Left Crane
48	Left Hawk

49	Left Crane
50	Left Dog
51	Willow
52	Praying Mantis
53	Leg Triangle
54	Drunkard
55	Praying Mantis
56	Drunkard
57	Praying Mantis
58	Drunkard
59	Praying Mantis
60	Drunkard
61	Praying Mantis
62	Drunkard
63	Praying Mantis
64	Drunkard
65	Praying Mantis
66	Leg Triangle
67	Eagle
68	Leg Triangle
69	Eagle
70	Leg Triangle
71	Eagle
72	Leg Triangle

LFA T'ai Chi Fan Movements

There are three hundred movements in our T'ai Chi Fan set. The first one hundred and fifty movements are fully explained in this book.
The Fan is the most demanding of all of our sets, it requires stamina balance and co-ordination.
The Fan set should be approached with care, listening to your own body because it involves stances which take place on the floor, such as Fish, Praying Mantis and Drunkard stances.
These stances will be familiar to students who have practised our K'ai Men exercises.
For people who are new to the Lee Family Arts and who are learning the Fan set purely from this book, please take the time to learn the stances first.
Ensure you use the warm up shown in our T'ai Chi Sword book, to prepare yourself for the movements.
It is important to listen to your body and that you do not strain; greater understanding comes from within.
The movements do not change, only your knowledge grows with the passing of time.
I hope you come to enjoy the Fan set and appreciate its depth.
This is only the beginning, the journey lasts a life time.

Starting Position

Start with both heels together in Eagle stance, your toes are pointing slightly outwards.

At the same time hold your fan in your left hand (see photograph).

Prepare

From Eagle stance take a pace off sideways to your left into Bear stance (feet shoulder width apart). It is important to place your heel down first. This is because T'ai Chi is based on Chinese Medicine; placing the heel down first allows the energy channels to open in the correct order.

Your fan remains in your left hand.

Number 1

From Bear stance draw your left foot to your right foot into Eagle stance (both heels together, toes pointing slightly outwards). Your weight should be evenly distributed between both legs.

At the same time transfer your fan to your right hand.

Number 2

Remain in Eagle stance for movement two.
At the same time fold your left arm across your body at shoulder height (palm facing down). With your right hand, open your fan so that the top of the fan is in alignment with your left arm (see photograph).

Number 3

From Eagle stance raise the heel of your right foot into Right Cat stance (bend your left knee slightly).
At the same time close and lower your fan with your right hand so that your fan finishes angled down towards your left hip. Your left hand is pulled back near to your left ear (archer), palm facing to the left.

Number 4

From Right Cat stance step forwards into Right Dragon stance. Remember to apply the principles of the Taoist Walk, it is important to have a good solid base to work from.

At the same time both arms extend forward at shoulder height. Your right hand opens your fan - sideways on.

Number 5

From Right Dragon stance drift your weight back into Right Duck stance. Remember to apply the principles of the Taoist Walk.

At the same time your left arm folds in at head height (your palm is facing away from you, your fingertips are pointing to the right). Close and lower your fan with your right hand, to finish with it pointing downward towards your left hip.

Number 6

From Right Duck stance step behind with your right foot into Left Duck stance. Remember to apply the principles of the Taoist Walk.

At the same time extend both arms forward at shoulder height. Your right hand opens your fan - sideways on.

Number 7

From Left Duck stance cross your right foot in front of your left leg into Right Crossed Legs stance (both knees are bent, the heel is raised on your right foot).

At the same time your left arm folds in at head height (palm facing away from you, your fingertips are pointing to the right). Close and lower your fan with your right hand, to finish with it pointing downward towards your left hip.

Number 8

From Right Crossed Legs stance turn ninety degrees to your left into Left Dragon stance. This is achieved by placing your right heel down and stepping with

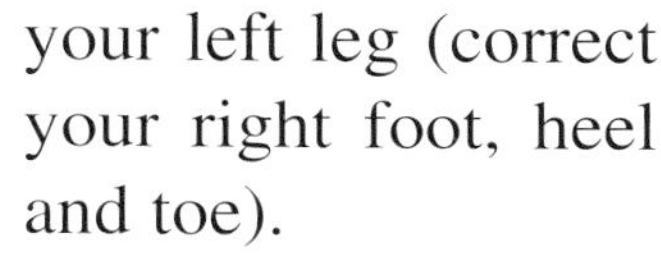

your left leg (correct your right foot, heel and toe).

At the same time both arms extend forward at shoulder height. Your right hand opens your fan - sideways on.

Number 9

From Left Dragon stance raise your right leg into Right Crane stance (right knee bent, your thigh is parallel to the floor).

At the same time fold your left arm in at head height (palm facing away from you, your fingertips are pointing to the right). Close and lower your fan with your right hand, to finish with it pointing downward towards your left hip.

Number 10

From Right Crane stance extend your right leg forwards into Right Dog stance.
At the same time extend both arms forward at shoulder height. Your right hand opens your fan (see photograph).

Number 11

From Right Dog stance step behind with your right leg into Left Duck stance (right leg bent, your left leg is straight).

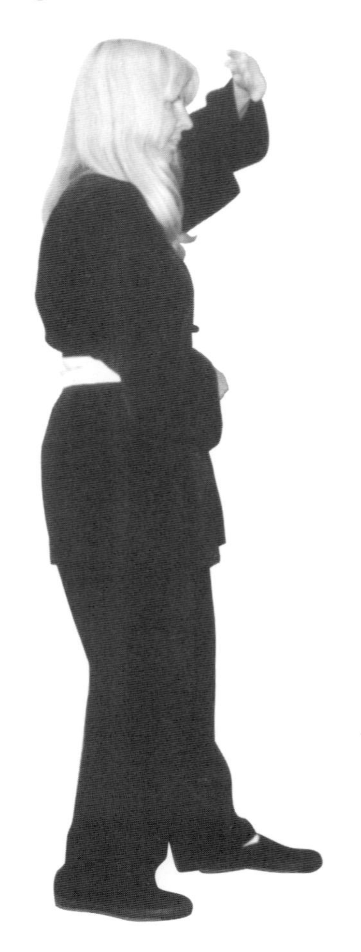

At the same time fold your left arm in at head height (palm facing away from you, your fingertips are pointing to your right). Close and lower your fan with your right hand, to finish with it pointing downward towards your left hip.

Number 12

From Left Duck stance step behind with your left leg into Right Duck stance (remember to place your left heel down first).

At the same time your left hand moves near to your left ear (archer). Your right hand opens your fan while your right arm extends forward at shoulder height.

Number 13

From Right Duck stance raise your left leg into Left Crane stance (left knee bent, your thigh is parallel to the floor).

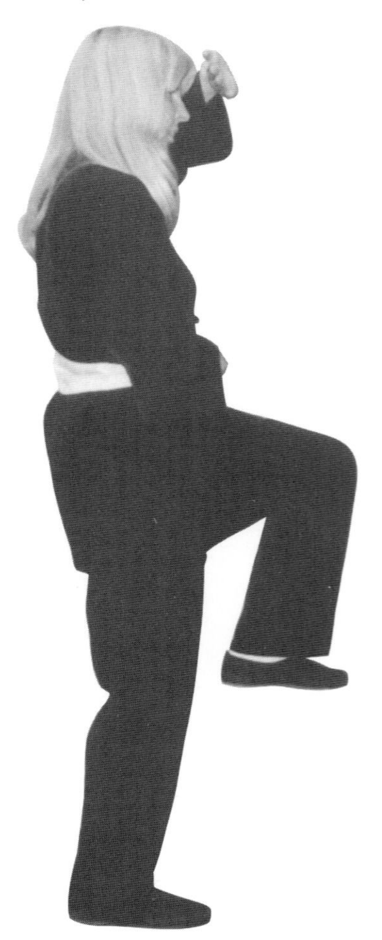

At the same time your left arm folds in at head height (palm facing away from you, fingertips pointing to your right). Close and lower your fan with your right hand, to finish with it pointing downward towards your left hip.

Number 14

Stay in Left Crane stance for movement fourteen as you turn one hundred and eighty degrees to your left. Your hands and fan remain in the same position as they were in for movement number thirteen.

Number 15

From Left Crane stance extend your left leg out sideways into Left Horse stance (keeping your right knee bent to aid your balance).

At the same time extend your left arm out sideways at shoulder height (your palm is facing away from you, fingertips pointing to the ceiling). Your right hand opens your fan in front of your face.

Number 16

From Left Horse stance move your left leg back to Left Crane stance.

At the same time your left arm folds in at head height (palm facing away from you, your fingertips point to the right). Close and lower your fan with your right hand, to finish with it pointing downward towards your left hip.

Number 17

From Left Crane stance swing your left leg out behind you into Left Hawk stance.
At the same time both arms extend forwards at shoulder height. Your right hand opens your fan (see photograph).

Number 18

From Left Hawk stance move your left leg back to Left Crane stance.

At the same time fold your left arm in at head height (palm facing away from you, your fingertips are pointing to the right). Close and lower your fan with your right hand, to finish with it pointing downward towards your left hip.

Number 19

From Left Crane stance swing your left leg forwards into Left Dog stance.
At the same time both arms extend forward at shoulder height. Your right hand opens your fan (see photograph).

Number 20

From Left Dog stance cross your left foot in front of your right leg into Left Crossed Legs stance (both knees are bent, the heel is raised on your left foot).

At the same time fold your left arm in at head height (palm facing away from you, your fingertips point to the right). Close and lower your fan with your right hand, to finish with it pointing downward towards your left hip.

Number 21

From Left Crossed legs stance take your right leg out sideways into Right Horse stance.

At the same time your left hand moves near to your left ear (archer), your right hand opens your fan as your right arm extends out sideways at shoulder height.

Number 22

From Right Horse stance move your right leg back into Right Crane stance.

At the same time fold your left arm in at head height (palm facing away from you, your fingertips are pointing to your right). Close and lower your fan with your right hand, to finish with it pointing downward towards your left hip.

Number 23

From Right Crane stance extend your right leg out behind you into Right Hawk stance.
At the same time extend both arms forward at shoulder height. Your right hand opens your fan (see photograph).

Number 24

From Right Hawk stance move your right leg back to Right Crane stance.

At the same time fold your left arm in at head height (palm facing away from you, your fingertips are pointing to the right). Close and lower your fan with your right hand, to finish with it pointing downward towards your left hip.

Number 25

From Right Crane stance swing your right leg forwards into Right Dog stance.

At the same time both arms extend forward at shoulder height. Your right hand opens your fan (see photograph).

Number 26

From Right Dog stance cross your right foot in front of your left leg into Right Crossed Legs stance (both knees are bent, the heel is raised on your right foot).

At the same time your left arm folds in at head height (palm facing away from you, your fingertips are pointing to the right). Close and lower your fan with your right hand, to finish with it angled downward towards your left hip.

Number 27

From Right Crossed legs stance step forwards with your left leg, lowering yourself into Left Chicken stance.

At the same time your both arms extend forward at shoulder height (palm facing away from you, your fingertips are pointing to the ceiling). Your right hand opens your fan (see photograph).

Number 28

From Left Chicken stance turn ninety degrees to your left into Drunkard stance (your left leg is raised vertically).

At the same time your left arm is extended vertically (palm facing to the ceiling). Your open fan moves round in front of your face.

Number 29

From Drunkard stance roll over onto your left side into Left Fish stance.
Your head is supported on your left arm (see photograph). Close your fan by the right-hand side of your face.

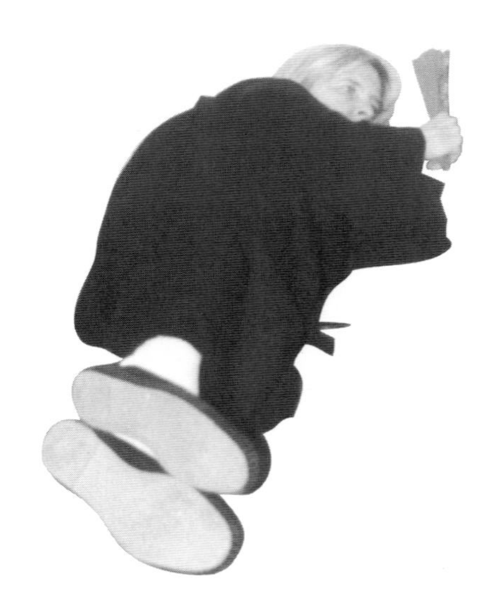

Number 30

Remain in Left Fish stance for movement number thirty, except that this time, raise your right leg into the air.
At the same time your right hand opens your fan adjacent to your face. Your left hand is still supporting your head.

Number 31

Remain in Left Fish stance with your right leg raised for movement number thirty one.
At the same time your right hand closes your fan near to your face. Your left hand still supports your head.

Number 32

From Left Fish stance turn ninety degrees to your left into Turtle stance (kneeling on all fours).
Your fan remains closed in this movement. Both arms are helping to support your bodyweight.

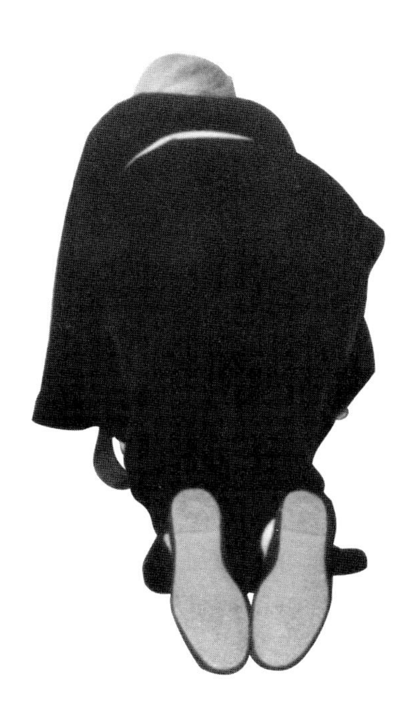

Number 33

Stay in Turtle stance for movement number thirty three except that you extend your right leg out behind you.

At the same time your right hand opens your fan as you extend your right arm forwards. Your left arm helps to support your bodyweight.

Number 34

From Turtle stance straighten your body into Praying Mantis stance (kneeling).
At the same time your left arm folds in at head height (palm facing away from you, your fingertips are pointing to the right).

Simultaneously close and lower your fan with your right hand, to finish with it angled downward towards your left hip.

Number 35

From Praying Mantis stance stand up into Left Dragon stance.

At the same time both arms extend forward at shoulder height. Your right hand opens your fan (see photograph).

Number 36

From Left Dragon stance cross your right foot in front of your left leg into Right Crossed Legs stance.

At the same time your left hand moves across to your right shoulder (palm facing in). Close your fan with your right hand so that it finishes at the right side of your face.

Note:- The photograph shows the front view, but the actual stance is with the back to the camera.

Number 37

From Right Crossed Legs stance step sideways (to your left) into Bear stance (feet shoulder width apart). At the same time your right hand opens your fan at the right side of your face. Your left arm moves to your left side (palm facing the floor, like in the T'ai Chi Dance).

Number 38

From Bear stance cross your right foot behind your left leg into Right Scissors stance (both knees are bent, the heel is raised on your right foot).

At the same time close your fan with your right hand so that it finishes at the right side of your face.

Your left hand moves across to your right shoulder (palm facing in).

Number 39

From Right Scissors stance step sideways with your left foot into Bear stance (feet shoulder width apart). At the same time your right hand opens your fan by the right side of your face. Your left arm moves by your left side (palm facing down, like in the T'ai Chi Dance).

Number 40

From Bear stance cross your right foot in front of your left leg into Right Crossed Legs stance (both knees are bent, the heel is raised on your right foot).

At the same time your right hand closes your fan near the right side of your face. Your left hand moves up to the front of your right shoulder (palm facing in).

Number 41

From Right Crossed legs stance step sideways to your left into Bear stance (feet shoulder width apart).
At the same time your right hand opens your fan at the right side of your face. Your left arm moves by your left side (palm facing the floor, like in the T'ai Chi Dance).

Number 42

From Bear stance cross your right foot behind your left leg into Right Scissors stance (both knees are bent, the heel is raised on your right foot).

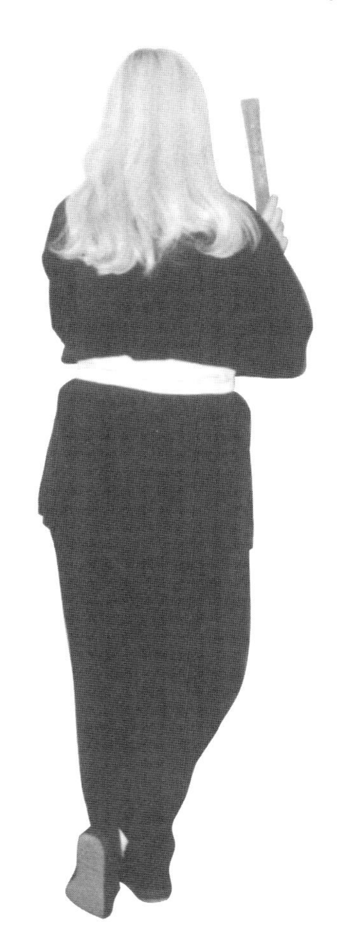

At the same time close your fan with your right hand so that it finishes at the right side of your face.

Your left hand moves across to the front of your right shoulder (palm facing in).

Number 43

From Right Scissors stance step sideways into Bear stance (feet shoulder width apart).

At the same time your right hand opens your fan at the right side of your face. Your left hand moves by your left side (palm facing the floor, like in the T'ai Chi Dance).

Number 44

From Bear stance cross your right foot in front of your left leg into Right Crossed Legs stance (both knees are bent, the heel is raised on your right foot).

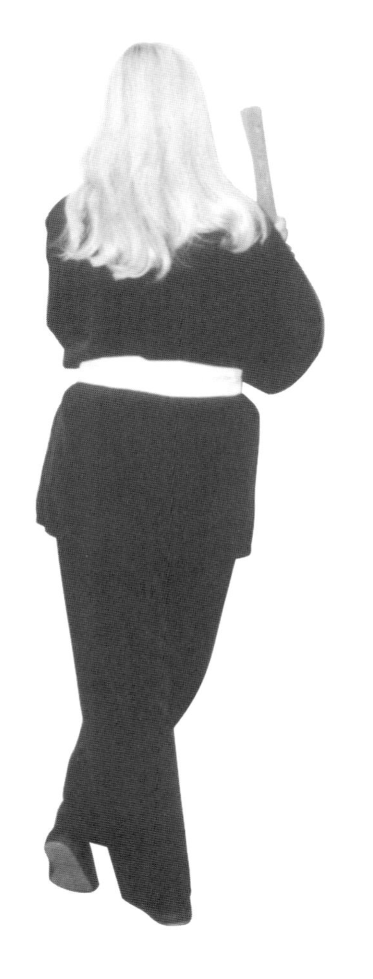

At the same time close your fan with your right hand so that it finishes at the right side of your face.

Your left hand moves in front of your right shoulder (palm facing towards you).

Number 45

From Right Crossed Legs stance step sideways with your left foot into Bear stance (feet shoulder width apart).

At the same time your right hand opens your fan by the right side of your face. Your left arm moves by your left side (palm facing the floor, like in the T'ai Chi Dance).

Number 46

From Bear stance turn ninety degrees to your left into Eagle stance (both heels together, toes pointing slightly outwards).

At the same time your left arm folds in at head height (palm facing away from you, your fingertips are pointing to your right). Close and lower your fan with your right hand, to finish with it pointing downward towards your left hip.

Number 47

From Eagle stance raise your left leg into Left Crane stance (left knee bent, your thigh is parallel to the floor).

Your hands and fan remain in the same position as they were in for movement number forty six.

Number 48

From Left Crane stance swing your left leg out behind you into Left Hawk stance.
At the same time extend both arms forward at shoulder height. Your right hand opens your fan (see photograph).

Number 49

From Left Hawk stance move your left leg back into Left Crane stance (your left knee is bent, your thigh is parallel to the floor).

At the same time your left arm folds in at head height (palm facing away from you, your fingertips point to the right). Close your fan as you lower it down to your left hip.

Number 50

From Left Crane stance swing your left leg forwards into Left Dog stance.

At the same time extend both arms forward at shoulder height. Your right hand opens your fan (see photograph).

Number 51

From Left Dog stance lower yourself down into Willow stance.

At the same time close your fan with your right hand and place both hands on your hips.

Number 52

From Willow stance roll over your right shoulder into Praying Mantis stance.
At the same time extend both arms forward at shoulder height. Your right hand opens your fan (see photograph).

Number 53

From Praying Mantis stance place both hands on the floor now jump into Leg Triangle stance.
At the same time fold your left arm in at head height (your palm is facing away from you, your fingertips are pointing to the right). Close and lower your fan with your right hand, to finish with it angled downward towards your left hip.

Number 54

From Leg Triangle stance turn one hundred and eighty degrees to your left into Drunkard stance (legs six inches above the floor).
At the same time your left arm extends vertically (palm facing to the ceiling). Your right hand opens your fan in front of your face.

Number 55

From Drunkard stance raise yourself up into Praying Mantis stance via Sitting Down Crossed Legs stance. At the same time close your fan with your right hand, both hands rest on your thighs.

Number 56

From Praying Mantis stance roll sideways to your right into Drunkard stance (legs six inches above the floor).

At the same time your left arm extends vertically (palm facing the ceiling). Your right hand opens your fan in front of your face.

Number 57

From Drunkard stance roll sideways to your left into Praying Mantis stance.
At the same time close your fan with your right hand, both hands rest on your thighs.

Number 58

From Praying Mantis stance roll sideways to your right into Drunkard stance (legs six inches above the floor).

At the same time your left arm extends vertically (palm facing to the ceiling). Your right hand opens your fan in front of your face.

Number 59

From Drunkard stance roll sideways to your left into Praying Mantis stance.
At the same time close your fan with your right hand, both hands rest on your thighs.

Number 60

From Praying Mantis stance roll sideways to your right into Drunkard stance (legs six inches above the floor).

At the same time your left arm extends vertically (palm facing to the ceiling). Your right hand opens your fan in front of your face.

Number 61

From Drunkard stance roll sideways to your left into Praying Mantis stance.
At the same time close your fan with your right hand, both hands rest on your thighs.

Number 62

From Praying Mantis stance roll sideways to your right into Drunkard stance (legs six inches above the floor).

At the same time your left arm extends vertically (palm facing to the ceiling). Your right hand opens your fan in front of your face.

Number 63

From Drunkard stance roll sideways to your left into Praying Mantis stance.
At the same time close your fan with your right hand, both hands finish on your thighs.

Number 64

From Praying Mantis stance roll sideways to your right into Drunkard stance (legs six inches above the floor).

At the same time your left arm extends vertically (palm facing to the ceiling). Your right hand opens your fan in front of your face.

Number 65

From Drunkard stance roll sideways to your left into Praying Mantis stance.
At the same time close your fan with your right hand, both hands finish resting on your thighs.

Number 66

From Praying Mantis stance place both hands on the floor and jump up into Leg Triangle stance.
At the same time your left arm folds in at head height (your palm is facing away from you with your fingertips pointing to the right). Close and lower your fan with your right hand, to finish with it angled downward towards your left hip.

Number 67

From Leg Triangle stance jump into Eagle stance (heels together, toes pointing slightly outwards).

At the same time both arms extend forward at shoulder height. Your right hand opens your fan (see photograph).

Number 68

From Eagle stance jump forwards into Leg Triangle stance (feet slightly wider than shoulder width apart). At the same time your left arm folds in at head height

(your palm is facing away from you with your fingertips pointing to the right). Close and lower your fan with your right hand, to finish with it angled downward towards your left hip.

Number 69

From Leg Triangle stance jump into Eagle stance (both heels together, toes pointing slightly outwards). At the same time both arms extend forward at shoulder height. Your right hand opens your fan (see photograph).

Number 70

From Eagle stance jump forwards into Leg Triangle stance (feet slightly wider than shoulder width apart). At the same time your left arm folds in at head height (your palm is facing away from you with your fingertips pointing to the right).

Number 71

From Leg Triangle stance jump into Eagle stance (both heels together, toes pointing slightly outwards). At the same time extend both arms forward at shoulder height. Your right hand opens your fan (see photograph).

Number 72

From Eagle stance jump forwards into Leg Triangle stance (feet slightly wider than shoulder width apart). At the same time your left arm folds in at head height (your palm is facing away from you with your fingertips pointing to the right). Close and lower your fan with your right hand, to finish with it angled downward towards your left hip.

Number 73

From Leg Triangle stance jump into Eagle stance (both heels together, your toes are pointing slightly outwards).

At the same time both arms extend forward at shoulder height. Your right hand opens your fan (see photograph).

Number 74

From Eagle stance cross your right foot into front of your left leg into Right Crossed Legs stance (both knees are bent, your heel is raised on your right foot).

At the same time your left arm folds in at head height (palm facing away from you, your fingertips point to the right). Close and lower your fan with your right hand, to finish with it angled downward towards your left hip.

Number 75

From Right Crossed Legs stance step sideways with your left foot into Bear stance (your feet should be shoulder width apart).

At the same time both arms extend forward at shoulder height. Your right hand opens your fan (see photograph).

Number 76

Stay in Bear stance for this movement, turn (jump) one hundred and eighty degrees to your left.
At the same time your left arm folds in at head height (your palm faces away from you with your fingertips pointing to the right). Close and lower your fan with your right hand, to finish with it angled downward towards your left hip.

Number 77

From Bear stance cross your right foot behind your left leg into Right Scissors stance (both knees are bent, the heel is raised on your right foot).

At the same time your left hand moves near to your left ear (archer). Your right hand opens your fan on the diagonal (see photograph).

Number 78

From Right Scissors stance turn ninety degrees to your left into Right Hawk stance.

At the same time close your fan with your right hand and place both hands on your fan, extending your arms forward at shoulder height.

Number 79

From Right Hawk stance swing your right leg forwards into Right Dog stance.

At the same time let go of your fan with your left hand, both arms extend forward at shoulder height. Your right hand opens your fan (see photograph).

Number 80

From Right Dog stance return your right foot to the floor before lowering yourself into Frog stance.
At the same time your left arm folds in at head height (your palm is facing away from you, your fingertips are pointing to the right). Close and lower your fan with your right hand, to finish with it angled downward towards your left hip.

Number 81

From Frog stance lower yourself to the ground into Drunkard stance (left leg vertical).

At the same time extend both arms vertically (your left palm is facing to the ceiling). Your right hand opens your fan (open side on). See photograph.

Number 82

From Drunkard stance roll sideways to your right into Praying Mantis stance. Note. You actually turn one hundred and eighty degrees in this movement.

At the same time your left arm folds in at head height (your palm is facing away from you with your fingertips pointing to the right). Close and lower your fan with your right hand, to finish with it angled downward towards your left hip.

Number 83

From Praying Mantis stance stand up into Left Dragon stance.

At the same time extend both arms forward at shoulder height. Your right hand opens your fan (open side on) see photograph.

Number 84

From Left Dragon stance step back with your left foot into Eagle stance (both heels together, toes pointing slightly outwards).

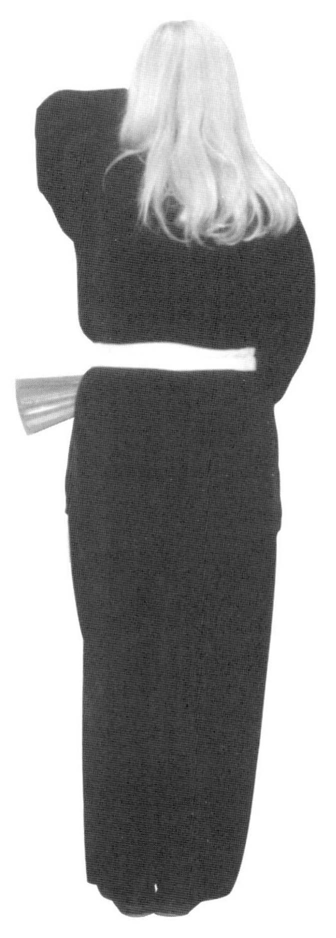

At the same time your left arm folds in at head height (your palm is facing away from you with your fingertips pointing to the right). Close and lower your fan with your right hand, to finish with it angled downward towards your left hip.

Number 85

From Eagle stance step behind with your right foot into Left Duck stance (right leg bent, left leg straight). At the same time both arms extend forward at shoulder height. Your right hand opens your fan (open side on) see photograph.

Number 86

From Left Duck stance step behind with your left foot into Right Duck stance (your left leg is bent and your right leg is straight).

At the same time your left arm folds in at head height (your palm is facing away from you, with your fingertips pointing to the right). Close and lower your fan with your right hand, to finish with it angled downward towards your left hip.

Number 87

From Right Duck stance step behind with your right leg into Left Duck stance (right knee bent, left leg straight).

At the same time extend both arms forward at shoulder height. Your right hand opens your fan (open side on).

Number 88

From Left Duck stance step behind with your left foot into Right Duck stance (left knee bent, right leg straight).

At the same time your left arm folds in at head height (your palm is facing away from you with your fingertips pointing to the right). Close and lower your fan with your right hand, to finish with it angled downward towards your left hip.

Number 89

From Right Duck stance step forwards into Eagle stance (both heels together with your toes pointing slightly outwards).

At the same time extend both arms forward at shoulder height. Your right hand opens your fan (open side on).

Number 90

Remain in Eagle stance for movement number ninety. At the same time fold your left arm in at head height (your palm is facing away from you with your fingertips pointing to the right). Close and lower your fan with your right hand, to finish with it angled downward towards your left hip.

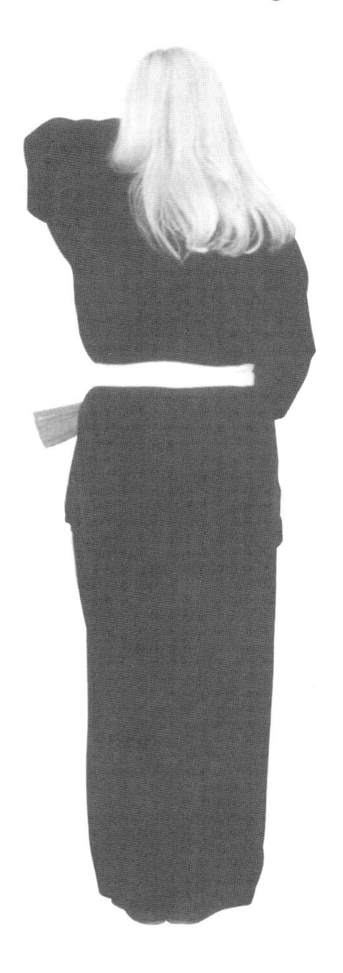

Number 91

From Eagle stance step forwards into Left Dragon stance.

At the same time extend both arms forward at shoulder height. Your right hand opens your fan (open side on).

Number 92

From Left Dragon stance cross your left foot in front of your right leg into Left Crossed Legs stance (both knees are bent, the heel is raised on your left foot).

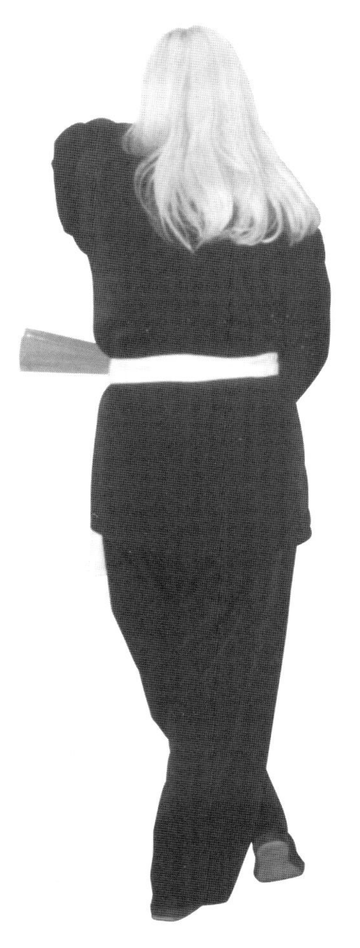

At the same time your left arm folds in at head height (your palm is facing away from you with your fingertips pointing to the right). Close and lower your fan with your right hand, to finish with it angled downward towards your left hip.

Number 93

From Left Crossed Legs stance turn ninety degrees to your right into Right Dragon stance.

At the same time extend both arms forward at shoulder height. Your right hand opens your fan sideways on.

Number 94

From Right Dragon stance step forwards with your left leg into Bee stance (both heels together, toes pointing slightly outwards, both knees are bent).

At the same time close your fan with your right hand and lower both hands to your hips (see photograph).

Number 95

From Bee stance lower yourself down and roll over your right shoulder into Praying Mantis stance.
At the same time, both hands finish resting on your thighs.

Number 96

From Praying Mantis stance turn one hundred and eighty degrees to your right into Lotus stance.
At the same time your right hand opens your fan (sideways on), your left hand also holds the fan (see photograph).

Number 97

From Lotus stance roll back into Willow stance.
At the same time let go of your fan with your left hand. Close your fan with your right hand as you place both hands on your hips.

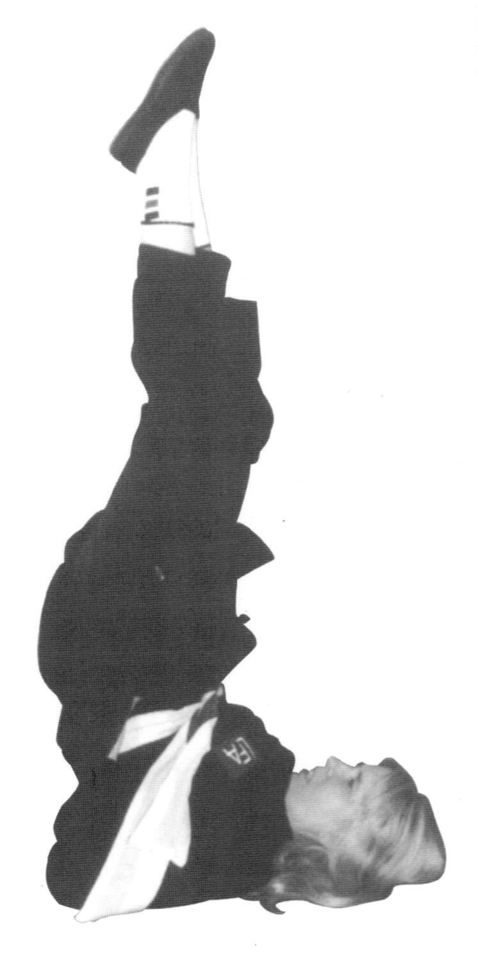

Number 98

From Willow stance roll over your right shoulder into Praying Mantis stance.
At the same time both hands move to your thighs, (your fan remains closed).

Number 99

From Praying Mantis stance stand up into Left Dragon stance.

At the same time both arms extend forward at shoulder height. Your right hand opens your fan (sideways on).

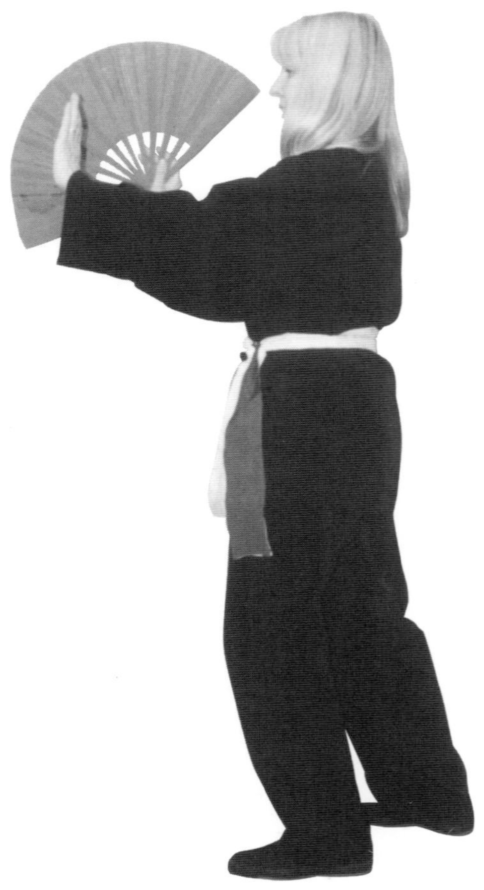

Number 100

From Left Dragon stance step forward with your right leg into Eagle stance (both heels together with your toes pointing slightly outwards).

At the same time your left arm folds in at head height (your palm is facing away from you with your fingertips pointing to the right. Close and lower your fan with your right hand, to finish with it angled downward towards your left hip.

Number 101

From Eagle stance turn ninety degrees to your right into Right Dragon stance.

At the same time extend both arms forward at shoulder height, your right hand opens your fan sideways on (see photograph).

Number 102

From Right Dragon stance step back into Eagle stance with your right foot (both heels together with your toes pointing slightly outwards).

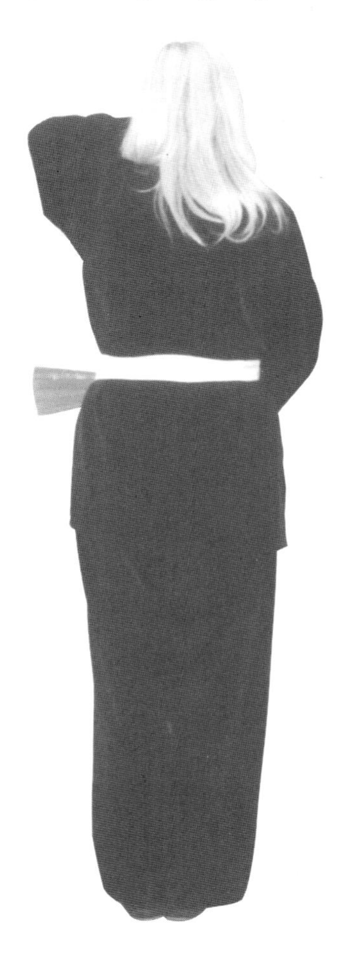

At the same time your left arm folds in at head height (your palm is facing away from you and your fingertips are pointing to the right. Close and lower your fan with your right hand, to finish with it angled downward towards your left hip.

Number 103

From Eagle stance step sideways with your right leg into Right Leopard stance (right knee bent, left leg straight).

At the same time your left arm extends sideways at shoulder height (palm facing away from you with your fingertips pointing to the ceiling. Your right hand opens your fan so that it is facing the front; you are looking to your left.

Number 104

From Right Leopard stance turn ninety degrees to your left into Right Stork stance.
At the same time your left arm folds in at head height (your palm is facing away from you and your fingertips are pointing to the right. Close and lower your fan with your right hand, to finish with it angled downward towards your left hip.

Number 105

From Right Stork stance extend your right leg out behind you into Right Hawk stance.
At the same time both arms extend forward at shoulder height, your right hand opens your fan sideways on (see photograph).

Number 106

From Right Hawk stance return to Right Stork stance. At the same time your left arm folds in at head height (your palm is facing away from you with your fingertips pointing to the right).

Number 107

From Right Stork stance extend your right leg out sideways into Right Horse stance.

At the same time your left hand moves near to your left ear (archer). Your right hand opens your fan to face the front at the right side of your face (you are looking to your right, see photograph).

Number 108

From Right Horse stance move your right leg back into Right Stork stance.

At the same time your left arm folds in at head height

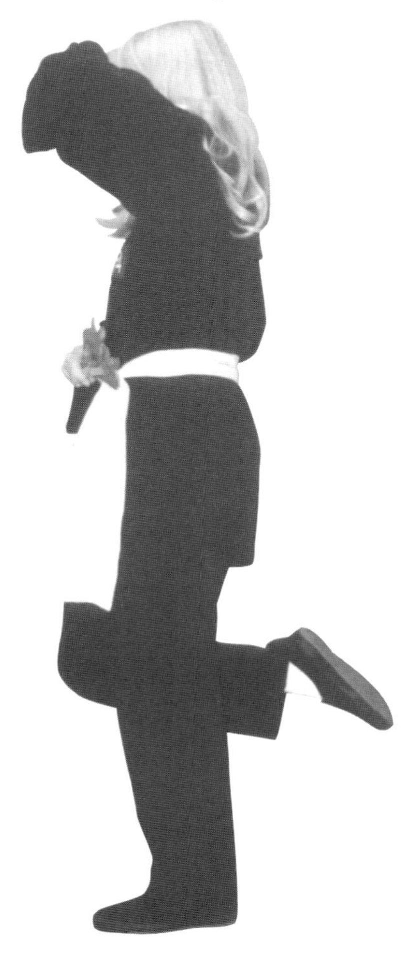

(your palm is facing away from you with your fingertips pointing to the right). Close and lower your fan with your right hand, to finish with it angled downward towards your left hip.

Number 109

From Right Stork stance extend your right leg forwards into Right Dog stance.
At the same time both arms extend forward at shoulder height. Your right hand opens your fan sideways on (see photograph).

Number110

From Right Dog stance move your right leg back into Right Stork stance.

At the same time your left arm folds in at shoulder height (your palm faces away from you with your fingertips pointing to the right). Close and lower your fan with your right hand, to finish with it angled downward towards your left hip.

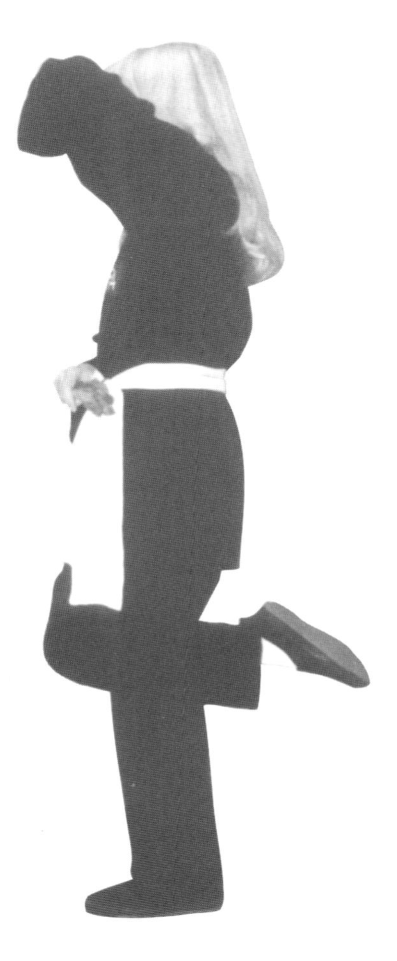

Number 111

From Right Stork stance turn one hundred and eighty degrees to your right into Right Dragon stance.
At the same time both arms extend forward at shoulder height. Your right hand opens your fan sideways on (see photograph).

Number 112

From Right Dragon stance raise your left leg into Left Stork stance.

At the same time your left arm folds in at head height (your palm is facing away from you with your fingertips pointing to the right). Close and lower your fan with your right hand, to finish with it angled downward towards your left hip.

Number 113

From Left Stork stance extend your left leg out behind you into Left Hawk stance.

At the same time extend both arms forward at shoulder height. Your right hand opens your fan sideways on (see photograph).

Number 114

From Left Hawk stance move your left leg back into Left Stork stance.
At the same time your left arm folds in at head height

(your palm is facing away from you with your fingertips pointing to the right). Close and lower your fan with your right hand, to finish with it angled downward towards your left hip.

Number 115

From Left Stork stance extend your left leg out sideways into Left Horse stance.

Your left arm extends out sideways at shoulder height (your palm faces away from you with your fingertips pointing to the ceiling). Your right hand opens your fan to face the front at the right side of your face, (you are looking to your left).

Number 116

From Left Horse stance move your left leg back into Left Stork stance.

At the same time fold your left arm in at head height (your palm is facing away from you with your fingertips pointing to the right). Close and lower your fan with your right hand, to finish with it angled downward towards your left hip.

Number 117

From Left Stork stance swing your left leg forwards into Left Dog stance.

At the same time both arms extend forward at shoulder height. Your right hand opens your fan sideways on (see photograph).

Number 118

From Left Dog stance move your left leg back into Left Stork stance.

At the same time your left arm folds in at head height (your palm faces away from you with your fingertips pointing to the right). Close and lower your fan with your right hand, to finish with it angled downward towards your left hip.

Number 119

From Left Stork stance, cross your right foot behind your left leg into Right Scissors stance.

At the same time extend both arms forward at

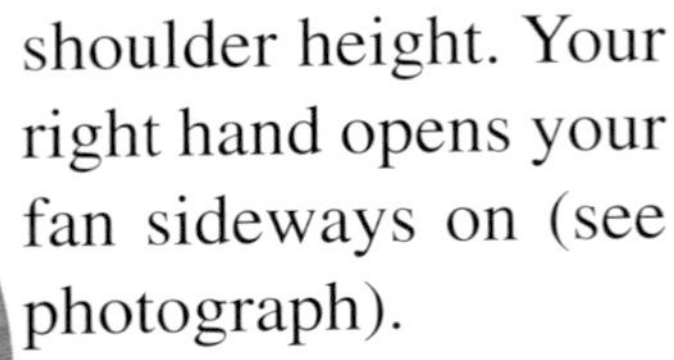

shoulder height. Your right hand opens your fan sideways on (see photograph).

Number 120

From Right Scissors stance sit down into Sitting Down Crossed Legs stance.
At the same time your left arm folds in at head height (your palm faces away from you with your fingertips pointing to the right).

Number 121

From Sitting Down Crossed Legs stance lay down into Drunkard stance.

At the same time both arms extend upwards. Your right hand opens your fan sideways on (see photograph).

Number 122

From Drunkard stance return to Sitting Down Crossed Legs stance.

At the same time your left arm folds in at head height (your palm is facing away from you with your fingertips pointing to the right). Close and lower your fan with your right hand, to finish with it angled downward towards your left hip.

Number 123

From Sitting Down Crossed Legs stance stand up into Eagle stance.

At the same time both arms extend forward at

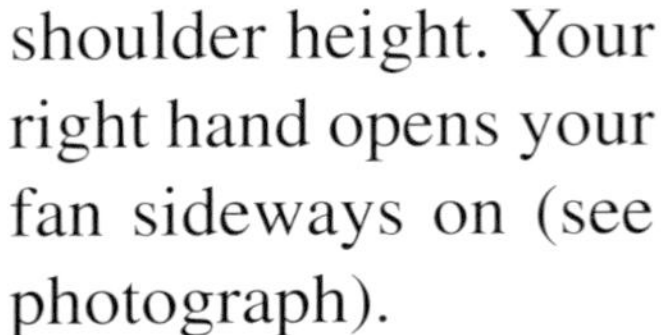

shoulder height. Your right hand opens your fan sideways on (see photograph).

Number 124

From Eagle stance step behind with your left foot into Right Duck stance.

At the same time your left arm folds in at head height (your palm is facing away from you with your fingertips pointing to the right). Close and lower your fan with your right hand, to finish with it angled downward towards your left hip.

Number 125

From Right Duck stance step behind with your right foot into Left Duck stance.

At the same time both arms extend forward at shoulder height. Your right hand opens your fan sideways on (see photograph).

Number 126

From Left Duck turn ninety degrees to your right into Right Leopard stance.

At the same time your left arm folds in at head height (your palm is facing away from with your fingertips pointing to the right).

Close and lower your fan with your right hand, to finish with it angled downward towards your left hip.

Number 127

Stay in Right Leopard stance for movement one hundred and twenty seven.

At the same time extend your left arm out sideways at shoulder height (your palm is facing away from you with your fingertips pointing to the ceiling). Your right hand opens your fan to face the front, (you are looking to your left).

Number 128

From Right Leopard stance turn ninety degrees to your left into Right Dog stance.
At the same time both arms extend forward at shoulder height. Your right hand opens your fan sideways on (see photograph).

Number 129

From Right Dog stance lower your right leg into Bee stance.
At the same time your left arm folds in at head height

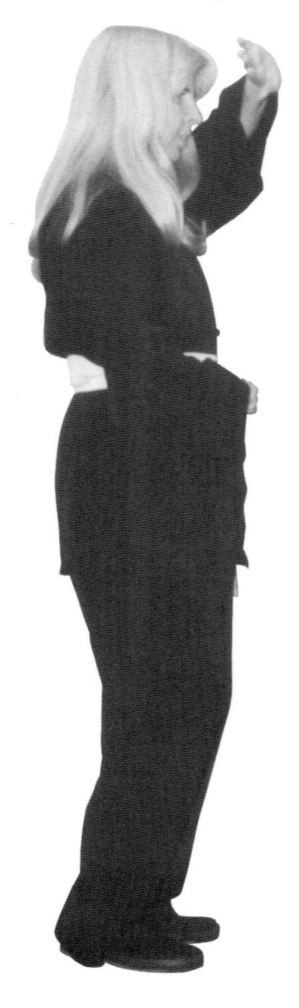

(your palm faces away from you with your fingertips pointing to the right). Close and lower your fan with your right hand, to finish with it angled downward towards your left hip.

Number 130

From Bee stance cross your right foot behind your left leg into Right Scissors stance.

At the same time move your left hand near to your left ear (archer). Your right hand opens your fan on the diagonal (see photograph).

Number 131

Turn ninety degrees to your left into Bear stance (feet shoulder width apart).
At the same time your left arm folds in at head height (your palm faces away from you with your fingertips pointing to the right). Close and lower your fan with your right hand, to finish with it angled downward towards your left hip.

Number 132

From Bear stance turn one hundred and eighty degrees to your left (jump) - still in Bear stance.
At the same time both arms extend forward at shoulder height. Your right hand opens your fan sideways on (see photograph).

Number 133

From Bear stance jump backwards (one pace) into Eagle stance (both heels together, toes pointing outwards).

At the same time your left arm folds in at head height (your left palm is facing away from you with your fingertips pointing to the right). Close and lower your fan with your right hand, to finish with it angled downward towards your left hip.

Number 134

From Eagle stance jump backwards into Leg Triangle stance, (feet slightly wider than shoulder width apart). At the same time extend both arms forward at shoulder height. Your right hand opens your fan sideways on (see photograph).

Number 135

From Leg Triangle stance jump back into Eagle stance (both heels together, your toes are pointing slightly outwards).

At the same time your left arm folds in at head height (your palm faces away from you with your fingertips pointing to the right).

Close and lower your fan with your right hand, to finish with it angled downward towards your left hip.

Number 136

From Eagle stance turn one hundred and eighty degrees to your right into Left Scissors stance (both knees are bent, the heel is raised on your left foot).

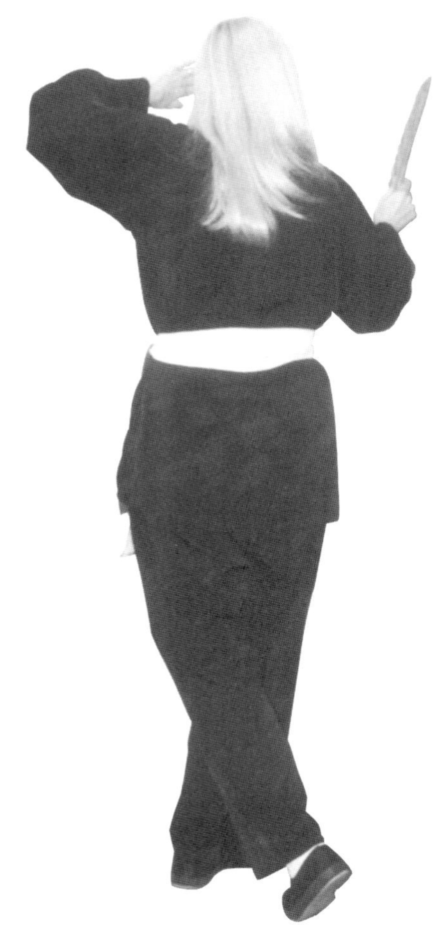

At the same time your left arm moves near to your left ear (archer). Your right arm extends forward at shoulder height, your fan is opened sideways on (see photograph).

Number 137

From Left Scissors stance step sideways into Left Leopard stance.

At the same time your left arm folds in at head height (your palm faces away from you with your fingertips pointing to the right). Close and lower your fan with your right hand, to finish with it angled downward towards your left hip.

Number 138

From Left Leopard stance cross your right foot in front of your left leg into Right Crossed Legs stance. At the same time your left hand moves near to your left ear (archer). Your right hand opens your fan on a downward diagonal at the right hand side of your body (see photograph).

Number 139

From Right Crossed Legs stance step sideways with your left foot into Bear stance.
At the same time your left arm folds in at head height (your palm faces away from you with your fingertips pointing to the right).
Close and lower your fan with your right hand to finish with it angled downward towards your left hip.

Number 140

From Bear stance cross your right foot behind your left leg into Right Scissors stance.

At the same time move your left hand near to your left ear (archer). Your right hand opens your fan on a downward diagonal at the right hand side of your body (see photograph).

Number 141

From Right Scissors stance step sideways with your left foot into Bear stance.

At the same time your left arm folds in at head height (your palm faces away from you with your fingertips pointing to the right). Close and lower your fan with your right hand, to finish with it angled downward towards your left hip.

Number 142

From Bear stance cross your right foot in front of your left leg into Right Crossed Legs stance.
At the same time your left hand moves near to your left ear (archer). Your right hand opens your fan on a downward diagonal at the right hand side of your body (see photograph).

Number 143

From Right Crossed Legs stance step sideways with your right foot into Bear stance.

At the same time your left arm folds in at head height (your palm faces away from you with your fingertips pointing to the right). Close and lower your fan with your right hand, to finish with it angled downward towards your left hip.

Number 144

From Bear stance cross your right foot behind your left leg into Right Scissors stance. This movement is the same as movement one hundred and forty.

At the same time your left hand moves near to your left ear (archer). Your right hand opens your fan on a downward diagonal at the right hand side of your body (see photograph).

Number 145

From Right Scissors stance step sideways with your left foot into Bear stance. This movement is the same as number one hundred and forty three.

At the same time your left arm folds in at head height (your palm faces away from you with your fingertips pointing to the right). Close and lower your fan with your right hand, to finish with it angled downward towards your left hip.

Number 146

From Bear stance draw your left foot into Eagle stance. At the same time both arms extend forward at shoulder height. Your right hand opens your fan sideways on (see photograph).

Number 147

Remain in Eagle stance for movement one hundred forty seven.

At the same time close your fan with your right hand as you lower both arms by your sides.

Number 148

From Eagle stance turn one hundred and eighty degrees to your right into Eagle stance (jump).

At the same time fold your left arm across your body at shoulder height (palm facing down). With your right hand, open your fan so that the top edge of the fan is in alignment with your left arm (see photograph).

This movement is the same as movement number two.

Number 149

From Eagle stance raise your right heel into Right Cat stance (bend your left knee slightly).

At the same time close and lower your fan with your right hand so that it finishes angled down towards your left hip. Your left hand draws back near to your left ear, (archer) palm facing to the left. This movement is the same as movement number three.

Number 150

From Right Cat stance lower your right heel and step sideways with your left foot into Bear stance.
At the same time extend both arms forward at shoulder height. Your right hand opens your fan sideways on (see photograph). This movement finishes in the same position as movement number one hundred and thirtytwo.

The LFA T'ai Chi Fan Set is for everyone. This book is more than a beginners' guide because for the first time in 3000 years, the first 150 movements of our Fan set, are in print for the benefit of the people in the West. The LFA retain full copyright on the movements in this book as they have not previously been available to the public.

To find the inner depth within the movements, you may wish to train with us at our ever growing number of LFA classes and day courses as shown on our Website.

I hope you have enjoyed learning the first one hundred and fifty movements of our Fan Set and look forward to meeting you in our classes and on our courses.

We intend to publish the remainder of the movements in a subsequent book in the not too distant future. May you continue to enjoy your journey with the Lee Family Arts.